I Love Myself

A Coloring and Activity Book
with Self-Love Affirmations

Volume 1

This Book Belongs To

GIANCARLON

I Love Myself:A Coloring and Activity Book with Self Love Affirmations

ISBN:978-1-7353806-3-6

Copyright © 2020 The Shana Danielle Company

Thank you for purchasing this love filled coloring and activity book from Ka'Maya Shanelle!

Inside you will find coloring and tracing pages to improve handwriting and teach compassion. This book was created in hopes that children my age will learn to love themselves and then release that love to others.

Young learners will love coloring the illustrations that showcase the beauty in everyone. They will also learn the benefit of affirmations by tracing powerful sentences like:

"I am amazing."
"I am brave."
"I am courageous."

Each coloring page is single-sided to prevent color bleed-through. I love to color in markers and did not like when the marker would ruin the illustrations on the back of my design in other coloring books.

I also loved when my mommy would hang my designs, so this layout is perfect for young learners to show off their artwork to **family.** Have fun coloring these beautiful illustrations while also accelerating your learning and education skills!

Enjoy **I Love Myself: A Coloring and Activity Book** with Self-Love Affirmations!

Love,

Ka'Maya

Ka'Maya Shanelle | ©2020 The Shana Danielle Company

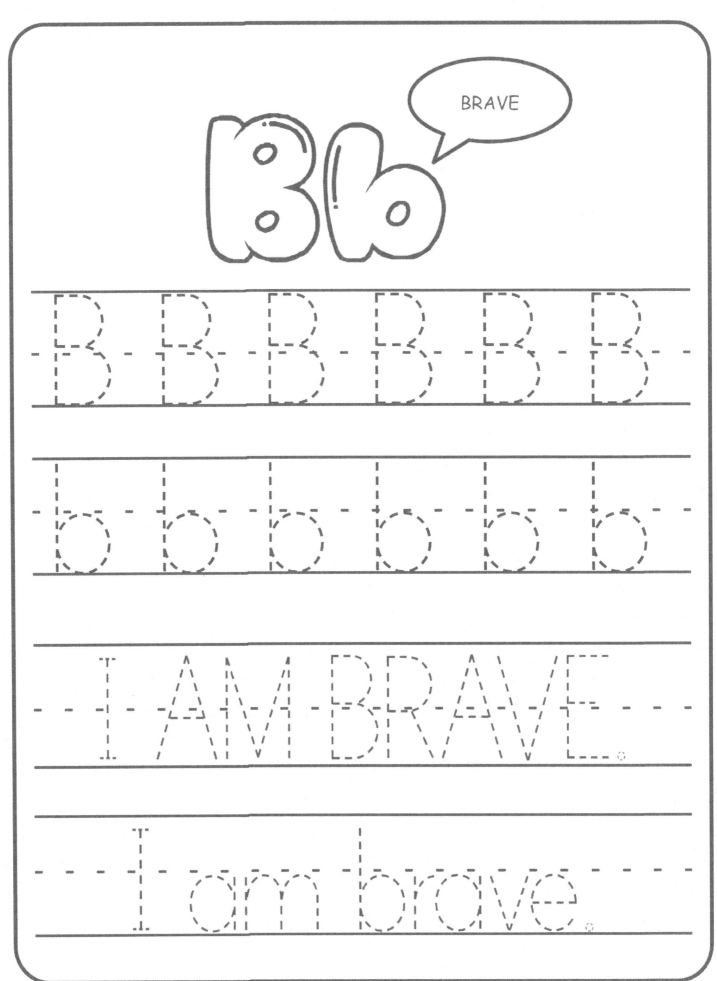

COURAGEOUS

Cc Cc Cc Cc Cc Cc

c c c c c c

I AM COURAGEOUS.

I am courageous.

I am Courageous

I am Excellent

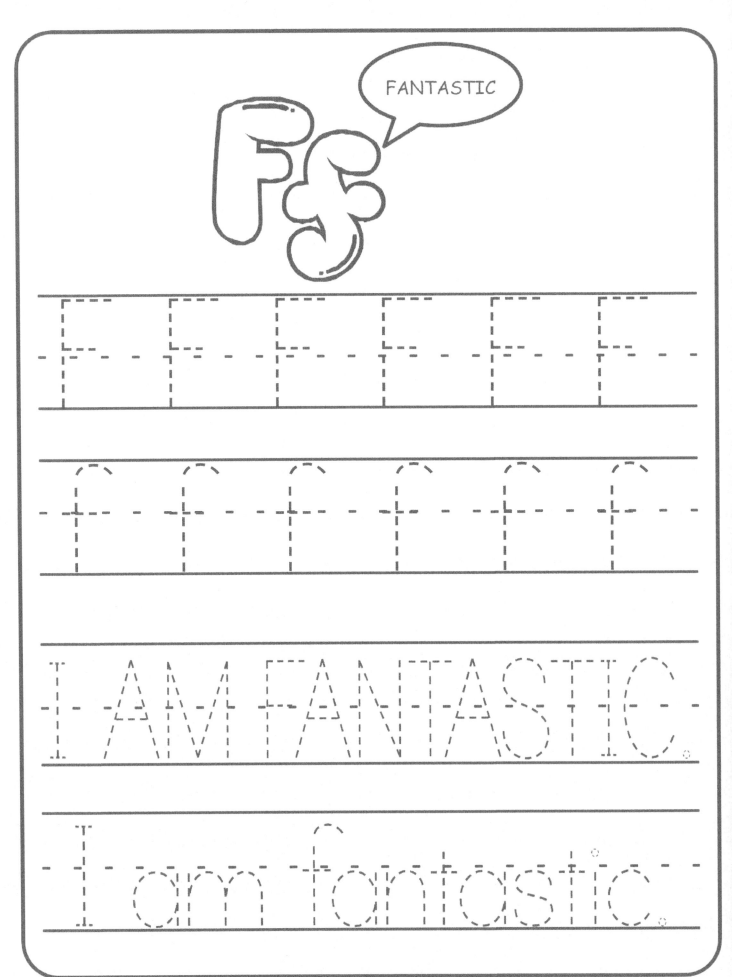

Ka'Maya Shanelle | ©2020 The Shana Danielle Company

I am Helpful

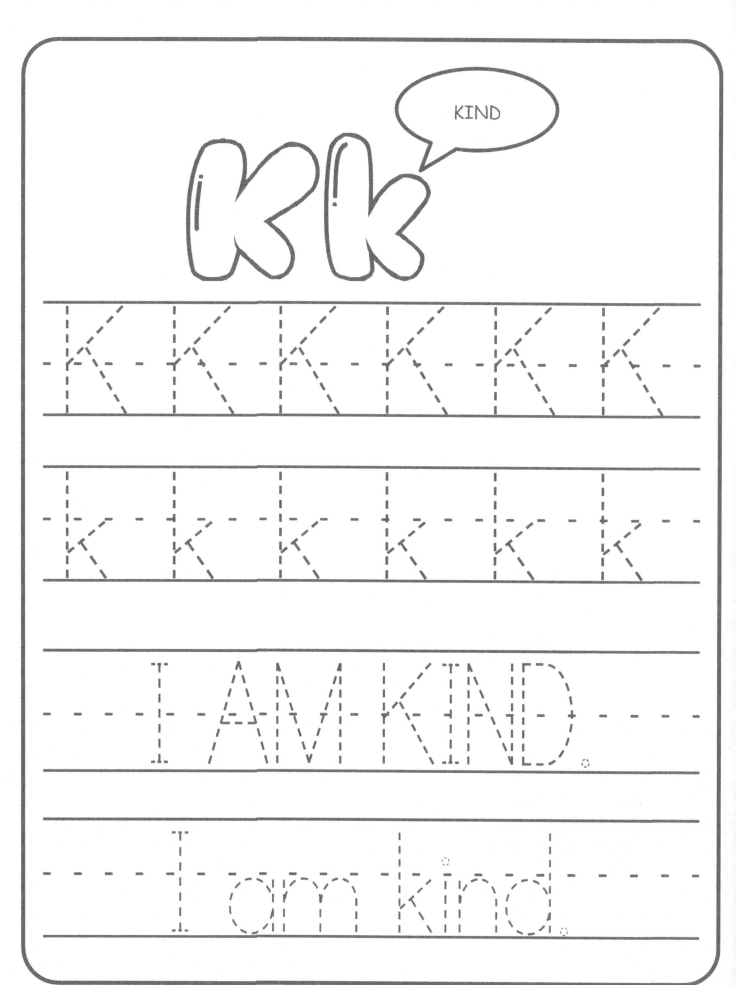

I am kind

Ka'Maya Shanelle | ©2020 The Shana Danielle Company

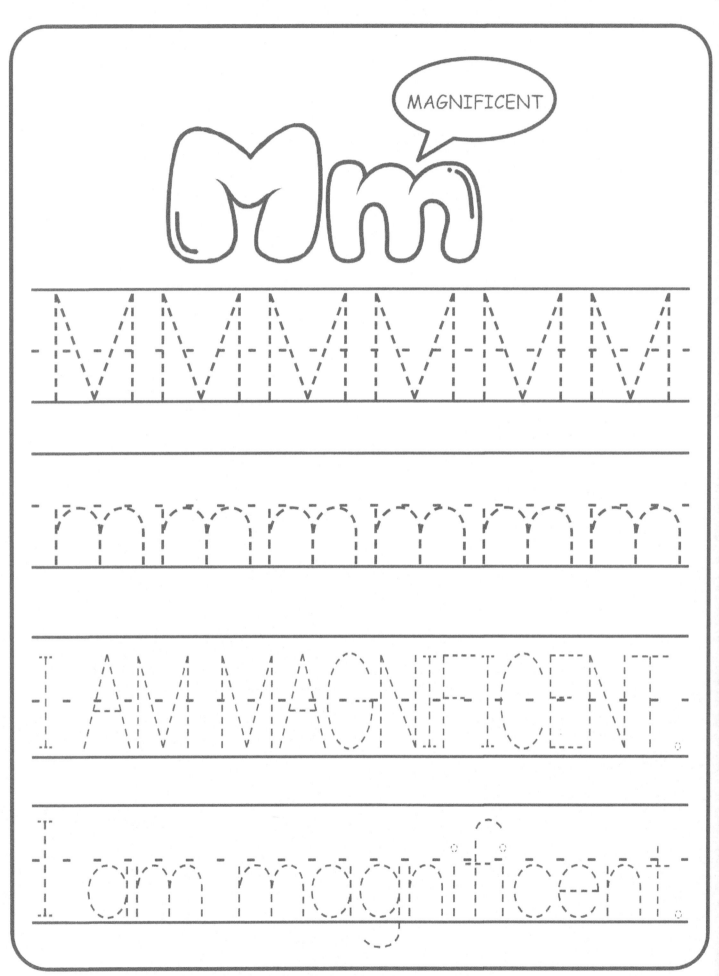

I am magnificent

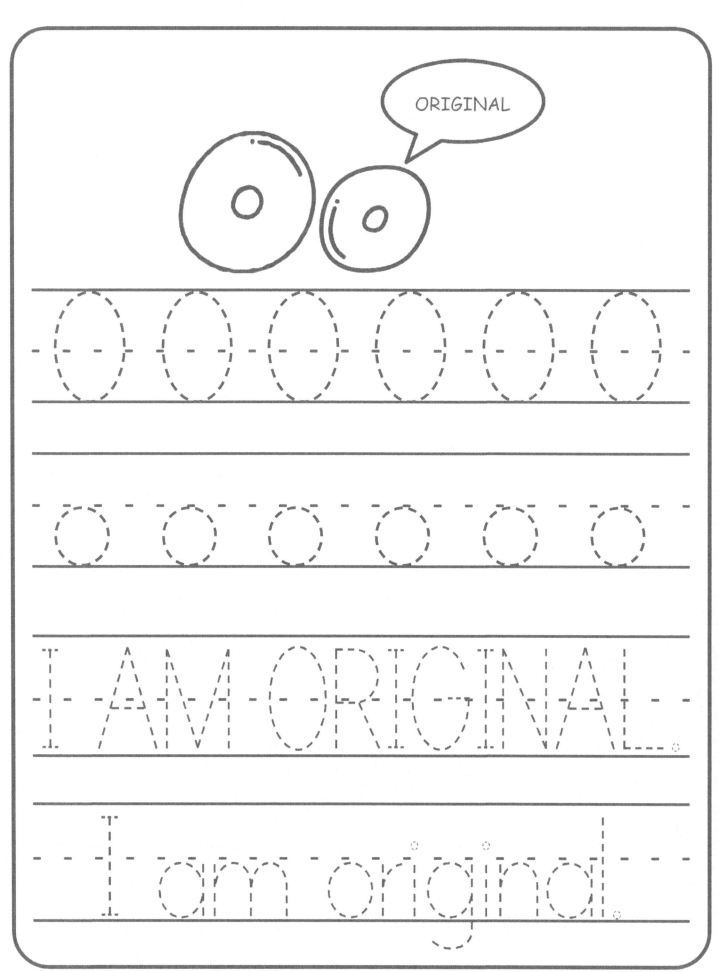

I am original

Ka'Maya Shanelle | ©2020 The Shana Danielle Company

Rr

RESPONSIBLE

R R R R R R R

r r r r r r r

I AM RESPONSIBLE.

I am responsible.

I am SMART

5 + 5 = 10

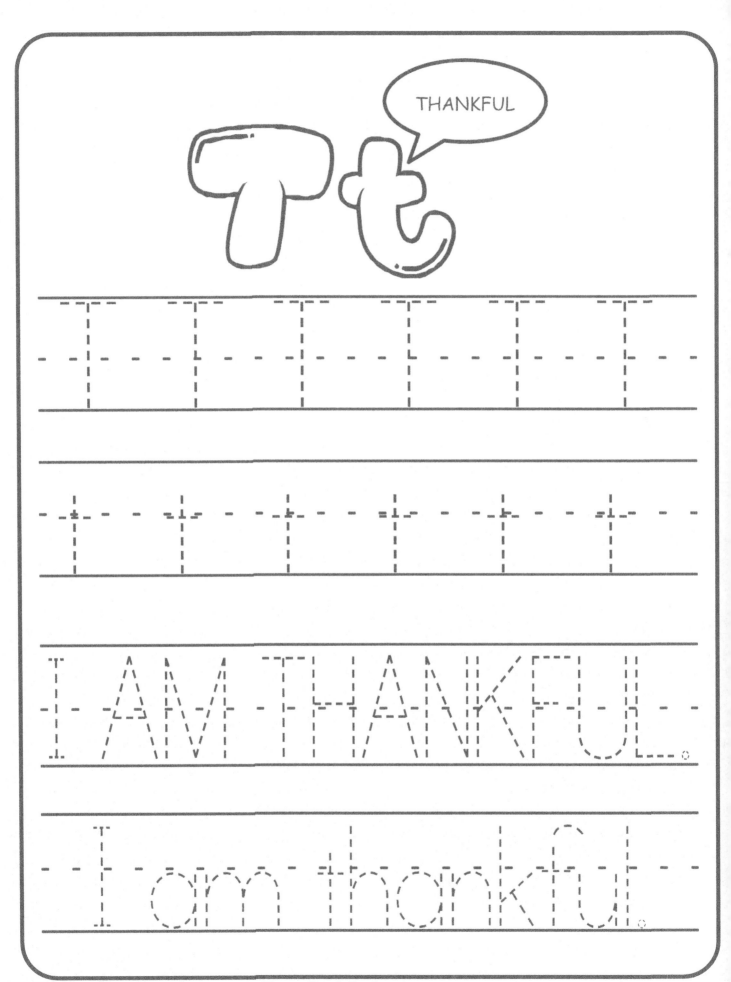

I am thankful

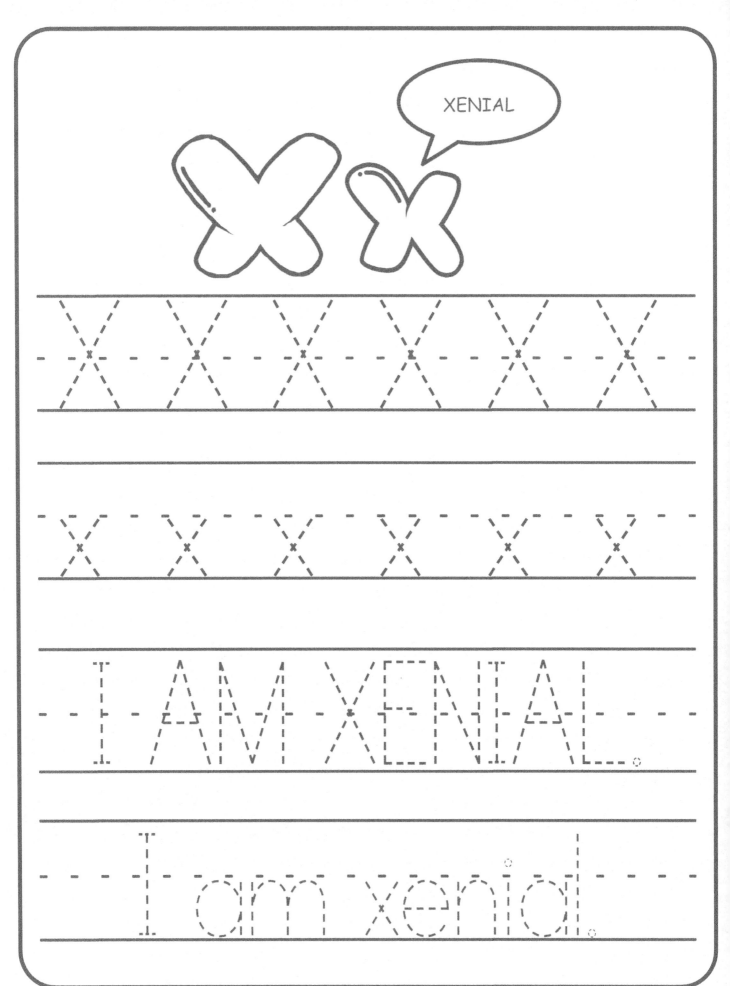

ZEALOUS

Z Z Z Z Z Z Z Z Z Z Z

Z Z Z Z Z Z

I AM ZEALOUS.

I am zealous.

I hope you enjoyed coloring and tracing all the pages in this book!

Remember to love yourself first and then extend that love to others!

For more fun, visit me on my website: www.KaMayaShanelle.com

You are Amazing!

Love Yourself
&
Never Stop Believing!

-Ka'Maya Shanelle

Made in the USA
Middletown, DE
26 April 2021